Daryl Cobb lives in New children. Daryl's writing began in jor at Virginia Commonwealth U man writing class inspiring and,

music and the guitar, he discovered a passion for songwriting. This talent would motivate him for years to come and the rhythm he created with his music also found its way into the bedtime stories he later created for his children. The story "Boy on the Hill," about a boy who turns the clouds into animals, was his first bedtime story/song and was inspired by his son and an infatuation with the shapes of clouds. Through the years his son and daughter have inspired so much of his work, including "Daniel Dinosaur" and "Daddy Did I Ever Say? I Love You, Love You, Every Day."

Daryl spends a lot of his time these days visiting schools promoting literacy with his interactive educational assembly shows "A Writer's Journey" and "Music & Storytime". These interactive cultural arts based performance programs teach children about the writing and creative process and allow Daryl to do what he feels is most important -- inspire children to read and write.

He is a member of the SCBWI.

Manuela Pentangelo lives in Busnago, Italy, near Milan, with her flowers, family and friends. She was born in Holland, but has lived all of her life in Italy. A student of architectural design, Manuela discovered that her dreams and goals lay elsewhere. She likes to say that she was born with a pencil in her hand, but it took a while before she realized that her path was to illustrate for children. Manuela often visits London, where she likes to sketch at the British Museum, and likes traveling to different places to find inspiration.

She is a member of the SCBWI.

Printed in the USA
1to2childrensbooks.com

MW00946454

The FROGS:
A Happy Life!

Written by
Daryl K. Cobb

Illustrated by
Manuela Pentagelo

10 To 2 Children's Books / Clinton

Written by Daryl K. Cobb
Illustrated by Manuela Pentangelo

Library of Congress Control Number: 2015908998

ISBN: 978-0-9849487-5-8

10 To 2 Children's Books

Time to Read

10to2childrensbooks.com

First Printing 2015

I dedicate this book to my parents and to parents everywhere. The transformation from babies to little people to young adults seems to happen in the blink of an eye or in a frog minute. Each stage is filled with amazing moments, but when all is said and done, the only things that are really important are that our children are happy, healthy and know we love them no matter what they do.

-- Daryl K. Cobb

To Daryl, who I love creating books with, and to all the children who will now get to enjoy this new one!

-- Manuela Pentangelo

Every frog
begins its life
swimming like a fish.

For you, a happy healthy life
would be my only wish.

So whether you grow up to be

FUN MIRROR

a big frog,

a small frog,

a lounging in the Sun frog,

a good frog,

a bad frog,

an animal-loving
fun frog...

there are so many
things that you could be!

You could have a
gift for song

and I will listen
all day long.

We might find out
you're speedy fast,

or a **frog**
who always
comes in last.

No matter how good or bad you do,
we'll be there to cheer for you.

I know there will be happy times,
and things that make you sad.

I know that there may be some days
you get a little mad.

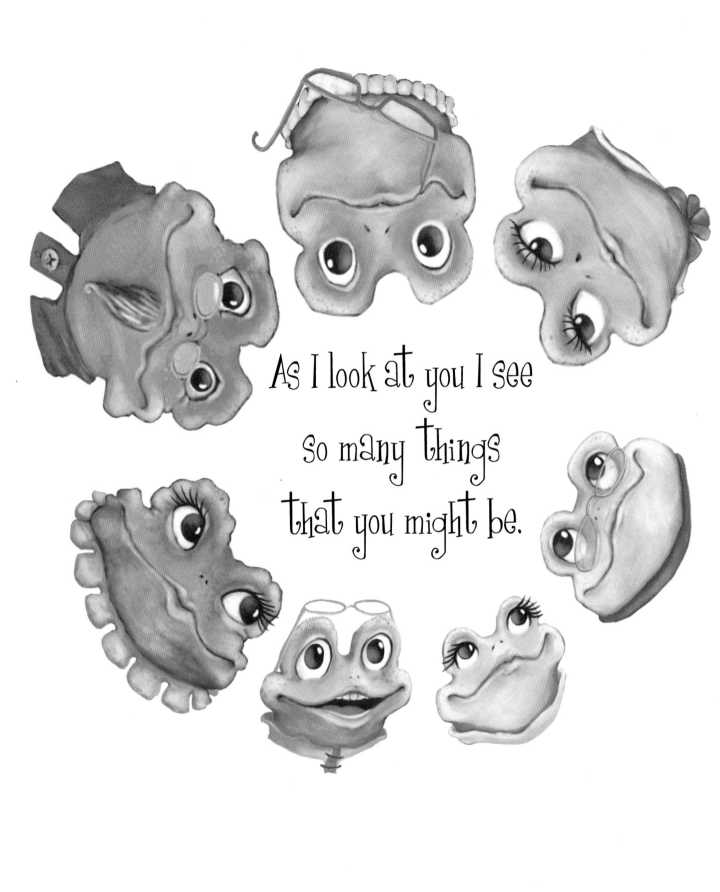

As I look at you I see
so many things
that you might be.

A chatty frog, a shy frog,
a thoughtful kind of guy frog,

a funny frog, a smart frog,
a not-afraid-to-try frog,

a helpful frog,

a teaching frog,

a best friend forever frog,

a playful little
brother frog,

a clever little
tree frog,

a tall frog, a short frog,
an I-can-do-it-all frog.

Some folks stare
at frogs with hair,
but individuality
must be met respectfully.

Maybe you're a B frog,
bringing home a C frog,

but a mom frog and a dad frog

love you no matter what.

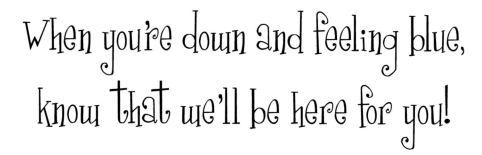

When you're down and feeling blue,
know that we'll be here for you!

Be an honest frog,

a caring frog.

Be friendly to your
fellow frogs.

But no matter what you do,
whatever you might be,

there will never be a frog
as proud of you as me.

Or me.
Me too, don't forget
about meeeee!

Pirates: The Ring of Hope

"Cobb's 14th book comes complete with pirates, mysterious messages and a magic ring . . .. The characters are rich and beautifully rendered, and the story is sprinkled with humor . . .. Much of the dialogue is delightfully silly. . . . [A] spirited swashbuckling tale of mystery and magic."

-- Kirkus Reviews

Mr. Moon

"A pleasing children's narrative with a relevant message. ... Cobb's text ... has a simple charm likely to please young readers [and]. . . Jaeger's illustrations give the night a soft, beautiful glow, complementing Cobb's text . . .. Her personifications of Mr. Moon and Mr. Sun are utterly delightful."

-- Kirkus Reviews

Daddy Did I Ever Say? I Love You, Love You, Every Day

"A cute, curly-haired, kindergarten-aged girl opens the story by asking her father if she's ever told him how much she loves him . . . the sentiment is sweet and Van Wagoner's illustrations are eye catching. . .. The verse Cobb has penned is appealing and . . . [t]he idea behind the story of the little girl and her doting father is charming[.] " -- Kirkus Reviews

Daniel Dinosaur

"A sweet story told in simple rhymes that young children will likely enjoy. Cobb and Castangno's cute, colorful picture book illustrates the bond between a brother and sister." -- Kirkus Reviews

Bill the Bat Baby Sits Bella

"A sweet book celebrating brother-sister bonds."

-- Kirkus Reviews

Bill the Bat Loves Halloween

"A fast- moving, fun rhyming picture book . . .."

-- Kirkus Reviews

Baseball, Bullies & Angels

"Cobb's long stretches of naturally engaging dialogue ... help deliver characters and twists that positively outstrip stories merely about athletic glory. ... Always sincere, occasionally shocking, this tale is required reading for kids and parents.

-- Kirkus Reviews

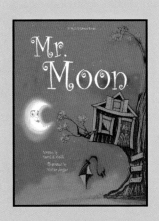

Children's Novels/Chapter Books

Pirates: The Ring of Hope

Baseball, Bullies & Angels

for advanced young readers
or ages 10-14 and up

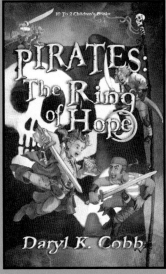

Books & Music by Daryl K. Cobb

Author Visits and School Program
information at www.darylcobb.com

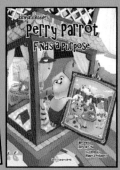

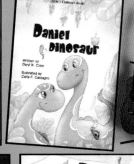

52341694R00023

Made in the USA
Charleston, SC
11 February 2016